THE FIRE BRINGER

The Paiute Indians live in Utah and in other states ranging to California on the west, to Oregon in the north, and as far south as Arizona. Long ago, the Paiutes told stories which explained the history of their people and the wonders of nature, the wide prairies, and the volcanoes of the Far West, now extinct. They thought of all things in nature as having life and personality. They told how the clever Coyote came down from the sky, found the earth, and prepared it for the first men. In the center of their small round huts, called "wikiups," still burns the fire which was one of Coyote's best gifts to the people.

THE
FIRE
BRINGER

A PAIUTE INDIAN LEGEND

Retold by MARGARET HODGES
Illustrated by PETER PARNALL

Little, Brown and Company
BOSTON   TORONTO

Books by Margaret Hodges

THE GORGON'S HEAD
THE FIRE BRINGER

Second Printing

T 10/72

The Fire Bringer has been adapted from a story in *The Basket Woman* by Mary
Austin, published by Houghton Mifflin.

"A Song of Greatness," translated from the Chippewa Indian by Mary Austin,
is from *Children Sing in the Far West*, published by Houghton Mifflin.

*Published simultaneously in Canada
by Little, Brown & Company (Canada) Limited*

PRINTED IN THE UNITED STATES OF AMERICA

For Eli Lilly

When I hear the old men
Telling of heroes,
Telling of great deeds
Of ancient days,
When I hear them telling,
Then I think within me
I too am one of these . . .

— "A Song of Greatness," translated from the Chippewa Indian by Mary Austin

The Fire Bringer was an Indian boy. The skin of his body was dark and shining, and he had straight black locks cropped at his shoulders. He wore no clothing but a scrap of deerskin belted with a wisp of bark, and he ran free on mesa and mountain. He carried in his hand a hunting club made of a cleft stick and a rounded stone.

He lived in the long-ago time before fire was brought to the tribes, when men and beasts could talk together, and understand each other.

The Coyote, keen gray dog of the wilderness, was the Friend and Counselor of man, and when the boy went out to hunt, the Coyote ran by his side.

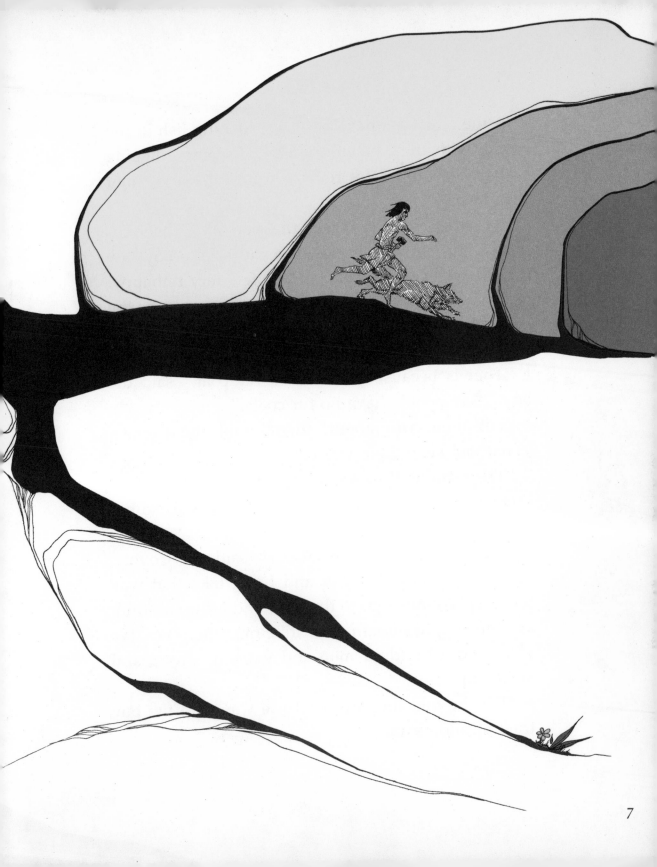

In the summer they saw men catching fish in the creeks with their hands. They saw women digging with sharp stones for roots to eat. In the summer they fared well.

But when winter came, the people ran shivering in the snow or huddled in caves. The boy saw that they were miserable, and he felt very unhappy.

"My people suffer and have no way to escape the cold," he said.

"I do not feel the cold," said the Coyote.

"That is because you have a fur coat," said the boy. "My people have no fur coats."

"Let them run about, then," said the Coyote. "That will keep them warm."

"They run till they are weary," the boy said. "And there are young children, and old people who cannot run. Help us, O Counselor!"

"There is a way to get help," said the Coyote. "It is very hard, but you and I will take that way together. We must go to the west and bring fire from the Burning Mountain. The tribe must help too. We will need a hundred men and women, strong and swift runners."

Then he told the boy what fire was, and the boy tried to understand.

"I will find the runners," said the boy. But that was easier to say than to do. Many of the people were lazy and many were afraid. Most of them did not believe the boy could help them, for they said, "We have never heard of fire. How can this boy know something that we do not know?"

But at last the boy talked so much about fire and the people were so miserable in the cold that they decided to do what the boy told them. A hundred men and women, the best and fastest runners, said they would go with him.

The Coyote advised them how the march should begin. He and the boy led the way. Next to them went the swiftest runners of the tribe, with the others following according to their strength and speed. They left the place of their home and went over high mountains where great jagged peaks stood up above the snow. They went down the other side of those mountains into a dark woods where the sound of the wind in the branches made them afraid. Here the Coyote stopped.

"Do not fear," he said to the people. "Take your rest."

In the morning he chose one man to stay in that place, saying, "Wait here until the fire comes."

"How will I know when I see it?" asked the man. "How does fire look?"

"It is red like a flower," said the Coyote, "but it is not a flower. You will know it when you see it." He led the tribe on toward the west.

The next night another man stayed where he was, and again the Coyote led the tribe westward. So it was at the end of each day's journey until they came to a great plain where the earth was dry and cracked and the parched grass rustled like straw. The Coyote chose a man to stay in that place.

"Rest here until the fire comes," he said. "But do not let it touch the grass. Fire can run raging through the grass and devour all before it."

"Is it a beast?" asked the man.

"No, it is not a beast," said the Coyote. "You will know it when you see it."

So they went on until only one runner was
left with the boy and the Coyote. And they came
to another range of hills, not so high but tumbled
thickly together and covered with a thick woods.

"Stay here," said the Coyote, "until the fire
comes." But the last runner asked, "Will the fire
come upon me like an enemy?"

"It can be an enemy," the Coyote told him. "It
is very fierce and hurtful and stays not for the
asking, yet if it is kept among stones and fed with
small sticks, it will serve the people well and keep
them warm."

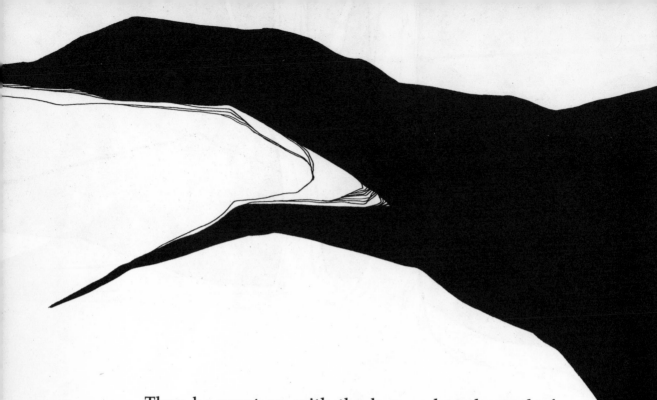

Then he went on with the boy and at the end of the hundred days they came to the Big Water at the foot of the Burning Mountain. It stood up in a high and peaked cone and the smoke of its burning rolled out and broke along the sky. By night the glare of the fire reddened the waves of the Big Water when the Fire Spirits began their dance.

"There is the fire," said the Coyote. "It has its lair inside the mountain and the Fire Spirits guard it night and day. Stay here until I bring you a brand from the burning. Be ready and right for running, and lose no time, for I shall be far spent when I come again, and the Fire Spirits will chase me."

Then he went up the mountain, and the Fire
Spirits laughed when they saw him coming. He
was thin, and his coat was much the worse for
his long journey. Slinking, shabby and mean he
looked, as he has always looked, and it served
him as well then as it serves him now. He looked
like an animal of no importance, so the Fire Spirits
paid him no heed.

Along in the night when they began to dance, the Coyote stole a blazing piece of wood and ran with it down the slope of the Burning Mountain.

When the Fire Spirits saw what he had done, they streamed out after him, red and angry, with a sound like a swarm of bees.

The boy saw the Coyote coming with the Fire Spirits after him. He saw the hot sparks stream back along the Coyote's sides as he carried the firebrand in his mouth and stretched forward on the trail, bright as a falling star against the dark bulk of the mountain.

Then the boy stood up in his place, clean limbed and taut for running. He heard the singing sound of the Fire Spirits behind the Coyote and the labored breath of the Counselor nearing through the dark.

The boy stood bent for the running as a bow bends to speed the arrow. The good beast panted down beside him and the brand dropped from his jaws. The boy caught it up. Out he shot on the homeward path and the Fire Spirits snapped and sung behind him. Fast as they chased him, he fled faster until he saw the next runner stand up in his place to take the firebrand from him.

So it passed from hand to hand, and the Fire Spirits tore after it through the thick woods and over the parched prairie until they came to the mountains of the snows. These they could not pass.

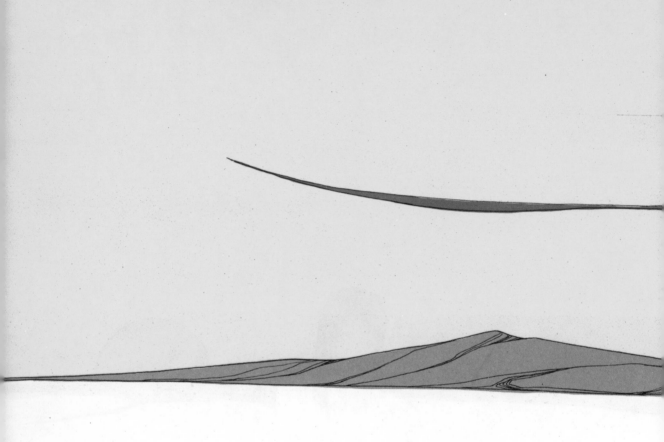

And the dark, sleek runners with the backward-streaming brand bore it forward, shining star-like in the night, glowing red through sultry noons, violet pale at twilight, until they came in safety to their own land.

Here they kept the fire among stones and fed it with small sticks as the Coyote advised, and it warmed them and cooked their food.

As for the boy, he was called the Fire Bringer while he lived. And after that, the Coyote was called the Fire Bringer, since there was no other with so good a right to the name.

And this is the sign that the tale is true. All along the Coyote's thin sides the fur is singed and yellow to this very day, as it was by the flames that blew backward from the brand when he brought it down from the Burning Mountain.

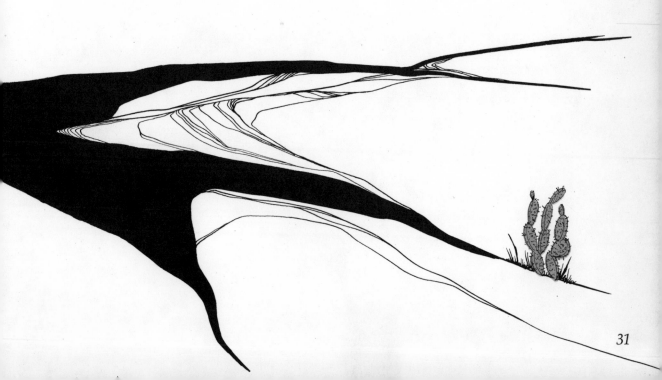